THE POETRY BUS

Poetry Explorers

Edited By Donna Samworth

First published in Great Britain in 2022 by:

Young Writers
Remus House
Coltsfoot Drive
Peterborough
PE2 9BF
Telephone: 01733 890066
Website: www.youngwriters.co.uk

Printed and bound in the UK by BookPrintingUK
Website: www.bookprintinguk.com
YB0490D

Foreword

Welcome to a fun-filled book of poems!

Here at Young Writers, we are delighted to introduce our new poetry competition for KS1 pupils, The Poetry Bus. Pupils could choose to write an acrostic, sense poem or riddle to introduce them to the world of poetry. Giving them this framework allowed the young writers to open their imaginations to a range of topics of their choice, and encouraged them to include other literary techniques such as similes and description.

From family and friends, to animals and places, these pupils have shaped and crafted their ideas brilliantly, showcasing their budding creativity in verse.

We live and breathe creativity here at Young Writers – it gives us life! We want to pass our love of the written word onto the next generation and what better way to do that than to celebrate their writing by publishing it in a book!

Each awesome little poet in this book should be super proud of themselves, and now they've got proof of their imagination and their ideas when they first started creative writing to look back on in years to come! We hope you will delight in these poems as much as we have.

Contents

Connaught House School, Westminster

Mariam Tovmasyan (6)	63
Calvin Dlubac (7)	64
Nayel Zubair (6)	65
Aria Gamage (6)	66
James Williamson (6)	67
Emeer Hamita (7)	68
Maxim Tinel (6)	69
Lara Sofola (6)	70
Allegra Kandel (6)	71
Maxine Gothland (6)	72
Mikayla Mizrahi (7)	73

Guru Nanak Sikh Academy, Hayes

Prabhnam	74
Gurfateh Sandhu (6)	76
Angad Vig (5)	77
Amitoj Dhariwal (5)	78

Mora Primary School, Cricklewood

Aidan Louie (6)	79
Theodoro Micoli Rossoni (6)	80
Zakariya Khan (6)	81
Eesa Hannan (7)	82
Klara Molodtsov Hay (6)	83
Emilia Savicka (7)	84
Theo Ball (6)	85
Michelin Reyes (6)	86
Hala Khan (6)	87
Bakr Alnzal (6)	88
Omar Fayez	89
Brian Malaj (6)	90
Daniel Andrisan (6)	91
Oumayena Aoun (6)	92
Aaron Daniel Perez (7)	93
Lovelle Cummings (7)	94
Maia Tabac (6)	95
Kaydan Gibbs-Young (6)	96

Israh Alkutubi (6)	97
Yunes Badri (7)	98
Jaicob Huxley (5)	99
Mohamed Mohamed (6)	100
Salma Al Thafiri Al Ghazi (6)	101
Beatriz Furlan Thomaz (6)	102
Abdullah Sardari (7)	103
India Goodman (7)	104
Anastazija Maric (6)	105
Jason Brook (6)	106
Carmina Dragan (6)	107
Zoha Jaffar (6)	108
Isabella Pampolini De Oliveira (6)	109

New Horizons Children's Academy, Chatham

Evie Rose (6)	110
Swayley Smith (6)	111
Harrison James (6)	112
Brooke Sanders (6)	113
Frankie Joe Walton (6)	114
Uzma Sebagala (6)	115
Lilah Fiddler (6)	116
Sam Kitchen (6)	117
Archie Funnell (6)	118
Jack Hobby (5)	119
Erica Sanders (5) & Ava Sofia Romanenco (5)	120
	121
Grace Hider (6)	122
Keilan Chiverton (7)	123
Ruby Groves (7)	124
Esmé Dale (6)	125
Marley Beale (6)	126
Ayden Sabondo (6)	127
Isabella Kerr (6)	128
Tanya Suetlomirova (6)	129
Harry McClelland (6)	130
Leon Roadnight (6)	131
Ava Leishamn (6)	132
Fredrik Hogan (6)	133
Imogen Still (6)	134
Sylvia Arnold (5)	135

Albie Leslie (6)	136
Jade Foreman (6)	137
Daisy Page (5)	138
Lehna Buparai (6)	139
Aarna Patel (6)	140
Nicole Eze (6)	141
Chase Whitmore (6)	142
Charlie-Junior Blair (6)	143
Ronnie Butler (5)	144
Georgina Philpott (6)	145
Efren Simpson (7)	146
Eloisa Tingley-Smith (5)	147
Busola Ogundiwin (5)	148
Jemima Caprice (6)	149
Jack Stevenson (5)	150
Dorothy Brown (5)	151
Amelia Norton (6)	152
Vivian Kisyova (5)	153
Sophie Goodchild (5)	154
Aretha Yeboah-Boafo (5)	155
Cassia (5)	156
Aston Edwards (5)	157
Muaaz Mazeen (6)	158
Sofia Georgieva (5)	159
Sofia B (5)	160
Jessica (5)	161
Maksimilian Kosenkov (5)	162

The Poems

Football

F avourite football team is Man City
O verjoyed when I score a goal
O ver my head the ball whizzes past
T eam player is what I am
B low the whistle and hear the cheers
A mazing at controlling the ball
L eft-wing is my preferred
L ose, I never do!

Sonny King (7)
Abernyte Primary School, Inchture

Hot! Hot! Hot!

I am hard but soft
Glowing red, I drip, drip, drip
Don't pour water on me
Or I'll turn to stone
I don't come out much
But when I do I explode
What am I?

Answer: Lava.

Rory Stark (7)
Abernyte Primary School, Inchture

My Favourite Animal

I live with grizzly bears
I am a type of wild cat
I don't hibernate
I have peach fur
I am a predator
I am the largest of the small cat species
What am I?

Answer: Puma.

Noah Bailey (8)

Abernyte Primary School, Inchture

My Senses Poem

Night looks like all of the streets are abandoned like a cave and twinkling stars shine as bright as diamonds.
Night sounds like black wolves howling at the sparkly moon and barn owls swooping down for their prey.
Night smells like strawberry lavender candles and fresh grass.
Night feels like getting under my duvet and cuddling with my dog.
Night tastes like warm tea and a midnight feast.

Maisy Goodridge (7)

Bessacarr Primary School, Bessacarr

Autumn

A is for rough apples ready to fall from trees
U is for umbrellas going up and down when it's
   raining in autumn and jumping in puddles
T is for toads hopping on lily pads in the pond
U is for underground they dig and dig until they
   get the treasure
M is for birds that migrate to a warmer place
N is for nuts falling off the trees.

Elliott Wigley (6)
Bessacarr Primary School, Bessacarr

Autumn

A is for autumn when we celebrate Halloween and Bonfire Night

U is for shiny umbrellas when raindrops are falling down

T is for birds travelling to another hot country

U is for hard, crunchy nuts underground hiding

M is for tiny, smooth mushrooms growing in dark woods

N is for dark, starry, spooky nights that get colder and longer.

Florence M (6)

Bessacarr Primary School, Bessacarr

My Senses Poem

Night looks like a dark shadow in the abandoned streets, whizzing around in the dark black sky.
Night sounds like wolves howling at the sparkling moon so the other wolf knows where to go.
Night smells like candles that have been blown out.
Night feels like a cosy blanket from head to toe.
Night tastes like warm hot chocolate because it helps me go to sleep.

Francesca Price (6)
Bessacarr Primary School, Bessacarr

Autumn

A is for smooth shiny acorns falling from the trees
U is for umbrellas in the cold weather
T is for toads jumping in the big pond
U is for new uniform to keep out the cold
M is for the gloopy, sticky mud when I go for a walk at night and I see the birds
N is for not much sunny weather, it is normally cold.

Maisie Parkes (6)
Bessacarr Primary School, Bessacarr

Autumn

A is for sweet apples falling to the ground
U is for umbrellas blowing in the wind
T is for brown trees dancing in the wind
U is for crunchy brown and red leaves under the golden tree
M is for small, white mushrooms in the woods
N is for spiky, hard nuts falling from a tree.

Erin O'Neill

Bessacarr Primary School, Bessacarr

Autumn

A is for ruby-red apples falling off the trees

U is for pink umbrellas that keep us dry

T is for fat turnips that grow in the wet soil

U is for the rabbits deep underground

M is for poisonous mushrooms that are in the woods

N is for the nights getting darker and longer.

Scarlett Willitts (5)

Bessacarr Primary School, Bessacarr

My Acrostic Poem

N oisy nocturnal animals scuttling through the crunchy autumn leaves

I n the night sky the black cat is on the brown fence

G littering oceans under the shining moonlight

H ooting from great big owls near the city looking for their prey

T winkling stars above me in the night sky.

Catrin Wilson (6)

Bessacarr Primary School, Bessacarr

My Senses Poem

Night looks like the streets are just a black line with shadows creeping along them.
Night sounds like a fierce wolf howling at the moon.
Night smells like nothing but invisible fresh air.
Night feels scary like when you are alone and lost.
Night tastes like hot chocolate because I am cosy under my blanket.

Sebastian Mundin (7)

Bessacarr Primary School, Bessacarr

Autumn

A is for acorns, all shiny and smooth
U is for umbrellas in the cold weather
T is for trick or treating on a spooky night
U is for school uniforms all warm and cosy
M is for sticky mud that I step in when I go to
school
N is for nests that birds sleep in.

Novah Blakesley (5)
Bessacarr Primary School, Bessacarr

Autumn

A is for apples falling off the trees
U is for umbrellas swaying in the wind
T is for turnips on the dirty floor
U is for crunchy, hard nuts buried underground
M is for tiny, quiet mouse finding a cosy place to sleep
N is for nuts that fall to the ground.

Dave Shelar (5)
Bessacarr Primary School, Bessacarr

My Senses Poem

Night looks like an abandoned street that's bare with shadows dancing along.
Night sounds like wolves howling at the dazzling moon.
Night smells like bubble baths that are toasty and warm.
Night feels like a fluffy warm bed.
Night tastes like doughnuts because they're hot and the night is hot.

Molly Roberts (6)
Bessacarr Primary School, Bessacarr

My Senses Poem

Night looks like a dark shadowy sky that has gold, glowing stars.
Night sounds like a quiet falling feather going down to the ground.
Night smells like dirty mud that's flying in the sky.
Night feels like it is raining ink from the sky.
Night tastes like doughnuts because they are a bedtime snack.

George Loveridge (7)
Bessacarr Primary School, Bessacarr

Autumn

A is for farmers collecting apples from the apple trees

U is for umbrellas going up and down in rainy weather

T is for children going trick or treating

U is for black moles that burrow under the ground

M is for the sticky mud

N is for names being called.

Charlotte Rossall (5)

Bessacarr Primary School, Bessacarr

My Acrostic Poem

N oisy tawny owls tweeting in the magical moonlight

I am looking at the fascinating twinkling stars

G liding bats swoop to catch their prey

H edgehogs are as sharp as a needle but sometimes it's hard to find food

T he little children carving pumpkins for Halloween.

Freddie Garvey

Bessacarr Primary School, Bessacarr

My Senses Poem

Night sounds like blowing wind in the scary night.
Night looks like sparkling stars in the midnight sky.
Night smells like thick smoke flying from the
crackling fire.
Night tastes like sweet hot chocolate making me
feel warm.
Night feels like my soft pillow that I rest my sleepy
head on.

Colin Haynes (6)

Bessacarr Primary School, Bessacarr

My Acrostic Poem

N octurnal animals are hunting for their prey in the pitch-black sky

I am looking at a camouflaged fox in the autumn leaves

G alaxies above me big and small

H ollow streets while foxes rustle through the dustbins

T he people are driving home to go to bed.

Frank Brentnall (6)

Bessacarr Primary School, Bessacarr

My Senses Poem

Night looks like a dark, empty street with not one footstep.
Night sounds like a silent owl flying in the midnight sky.
Night smells like a breeze coming from your window.
Night feels like black wind floating across you.
Night tastes like warm melted marshmallows and hot chocolate.

Lilly McGuirk-Wright (6)

Bessacarr Primary School, Bessacarr

Night Poem

N octurnal foxes come out at night
I nside we are home with teddies
G limmering stars fly through the night sparkling
H ooting owls in the night outside
T here's rustling at night keeping me awake but I don't care as I'm happy at night.

Hetti Howard (6)

Bessacarr Primary School, Bessacarr

Autumn

A is for apples on the wet ground
U is for plastic umbrellas in the rain
T is for tall trees swaying in the wind
U is for crunchy leaves under the ground
M is for mice finding places to sleep
N is for nuts hiding under the ground.

Flo Fleming (5)
Bessacarr Primary School, Bessacarr

Autumn

A is for farmers collecting apples on apple trees
U is for umbrellas going up and down in rainy weather
T is for going trick or treating
U is for the black voles underground
M is for the slimy mud
N is for nuts falling every day.

Matthew Sheehan (5)
Bessacarr Primary School, Bessacarr

Autumn

A is for juicy sweet apples that fall from the ground

U is for umbrellas we use in the rain

T is for tree swaying in the rain

U is for crunchy leaves under the swaying trees

M is for mice underground

N is for nuts underground.

Reuben Goodlad (6)

Bessacarr Primary School, Bessacarr

My Senses Poem

Night looks like fuel that you put in your car.
Night sounds like a barn owl flying really gracefully.
Night smells like a hot chocolate right beside my bed.
Night feels like creepy monsters creeping up on you.
Night tastes like hot chocolate so I can dream of chocolate.

Elliott Johnson (6)
Bessacarr Primary School, Bessacarr

My Acrostic Poem

N ot a single sound can be heard on the dusky streets

I n the terrifying night sky, no one can be seen

G littering, big, shiny stars glowing in the sky

H uge wolves are getting their slow prey

T he little babies screeching and screaming.

Teddy Biltcliffe (6)

Bessacarr Primary School, Bessacarr

Autumn

A is for autumn when we celebrate Halloween
U is for umbrella when it is windy
T is for birds travelling to hot countries
U is for rabbits hiding underground
M is for mice finding warm places
N is for spiky, hard nuts.

Fletcher
Bessacarr Primary School, Bessacarr

My Senses Poem

Night looks like an abandoned street with no sight of cars or people.
Night sounds like ghostly shadows appearing at night.
Night smells like a strawberry and vanilla candle being blown out.
Night feels like a ghost town.
Night tastes like delicious hot chocolate.

Jonas Smalstys (6)

Bessacarr Primary School, Bessacarr

Autumn

A is for acorns falling from the tree
U is for umbrellas keeping us dry
T is for small orange turnips in the wet mud
U is for uniform to keep me warm
M is for sticky mud in the woods
N is for nuts that squirrels eat.

Otto Clarke (5)
Bessacarr Primary School, Bessacarr

My Acrostic Poem

N obody can be seen in the gloomy town

I n the light, nocturnal animals go hunting

G reat big barn owls swooping as quietly as a mouse

H edges swaying and trees blowing in the strong wind

T ired owls fall asleep on a swaying branch.

Erin O'Mahoney

Bessacarr Primary School, Bessacarr

My Senses Poem

Night looks like a beautiful dark shadow.
Night sounds like an owl tweeting in the pitch-black night.
Night smells like smoke when I blow out the candles.
Night feels like a fluffy blanket so I go to sleep.
Night tastes like dark marshmallows and hot chocolate.

Grace Skidmore (6)

Bessacarr Primary School, Bessacarr

My Senses Poem

Night looks like a round, white beautiful moon in the dark black sky.
Night sounds like a screeching barn owl.
Night smells like a candle being blown out.
Night feels like a comfy warm blanket around me.
Night tastes like fresh doughnuts and hot chocolate.

Fletcher Lambert (6)
Bessacarr Primary School, Bessacarr

Autumn

A is for very crunchy apples.
U is for umbrella in the cold wet weather
T is for the trees with the autumn leaves
U is for very cosy uniforms
M is for gloopy, sticky mud in the forest
N is for very hard nuts.

Willow Brown (5)
Bessacarr Primary School, Bessacarr

My Acrostic Poem

N ight is useful to the nocturnal animals
I n my bed I am snuggled up tight in my fluffy blanket
G listening roads, not even a sound to be heard
H edgehogs come out at night
T winkling stars shine in the dark night sky.

George Wilson
Bessacarr Primary School, Bessacarr

My Acrostic Poem

N octurnal animals are pouncing on their prey
I am staring at the interesting, twinkling bright stars
G reat Big Ben strikes midnight
H ollow skies and no noise to spare
T he tawny owls are shooting in the dark sky.

Freddie Stone (6)
Bessacarr Primary School, Bessacarr

My Senses Poem

Night looks like ink sprinkling across the sky.
Night sounds like hooting owls in the midnight darkness.
Night sounds like my mummy cooking tea.
Night feels like a warm cosy bed that is like a fluffy cloud.
Night tastes like a warm hot chocolate.

Joshua Rice-Kelly
Bessacarr Primary School, Bessacarr

Night Poem

In the night I see the moon shimmering in the sky
In the night I hear aeroplanes zooming in the sky
In the night I feel a hot-water bottle keeping me
warm
In the night I smell food cooking
In the night I taste sweets making a lovely taste.

Aaila Noor (6)
Bessacarr Primary School, Bessacarr

My Senses Poem

Night smells like a candle blown out beside my bed.
Night tastes like pumpkins because they are spooky and scary.
Night looks as black as a school shoe.
Night sounds like a hungry hooting owl.
Night feels like a soft blanket over my head.

Phoebie Bennett

Bessacarr Primary School, Bessacarr

My Senses Poem

Night looks like a graceful star glimmering in the sky.
Night sounds like a howling wolf in the dark.
Night smells like smoke floating into the sky.
Night feels like a soft, fluffy mouse in my hands.
Night tastes like a fresh doughnut.

Eryn Avill
Bessacarr Primary School, Bessacarr

My Senses Poem

Night looks like a dark mysterious sky with not a single soul.
Night sounds like not a footstep around.
Night smells like a nice cup of tea and a chocolate pudding.
Night feels like a cosy warm blanket.
Night tastes like ice cream.

Oscar Roberts (6)
Bessacarr Primary School, Bessacarr

My Senses Poem

Night looks like dark shadows.
Night sounds like owls tweeting in the night.
Night smells like lavender that helps me get to sleep.
Night feels like a comfy blanket which is a deep dark blue.
Night tastes like delicious hot dogs.

Olivia Burnitt
Bessacarr Primary School, Bessacarr

My Senses Poem

Night looks like shooting stars in the sky.
Night sounds like a wolf howling at the moon.
Night smells like hot chocolate next to me.
Night feels as soft as a blanket.
Night tastes like dark chocolate because it is like midnight.

Louis Hodge (7)
Bessacarr Primary School, Bessacarr

Night Poem

I can see a wolf
I can see a fox
I can smell hot chocolate
I can smell pizza
I can feel tea
I can feel blankets
I can smell pizza
I can smell marshmallows
I can hear rustles
I can hear foxes.

Marty Barber (6)
Bessacarr Primary School, Bessacarr

My Senses Poem

Night looks like shiny stars glittering.
Night sounds like owls hooting in the dark sky.
Night smells like cake and hot chocolate.
Night feels like a soft marshmallow bed.
Night tastes like warm chocolate doughnuts.

Abdul Subhan Hashmi (6)
Bessacarr Primary School, Bessacarr

Night Poem

N oisy foxes are scrambling in the night
I nvisible black clouds in the dark
G iant bears are soft and fluffy
H igh up in the sky owls are flying
T ime for me and my teddy to go to bed.

Zara Crosby (6)
Bessacarr Primary School, Bessacarr

Night Poem

In the night I hear naughty foxes
I smell hot chocolate and it makes me hungry
I smell a grassy smell and it is nice
I shiver in the cold and the crispy leaves
I hear noises and the naughty foxes.

Keni Singh (6)
Bessacarr Primary School, Bessacarr

My Senses Poem

Night looks like sparkly golden stars.
Night sounds like owls hooting in the midnight.
Night smells like fresh air.
Night feels like soft pillows.
Night tastes like sprinkly doughnuts.

Ryan Heydarzadeh Charchi (6)

Bessacarr Primary School, Bessacarr

My Senses Poem

Night looks like the moon is glowing.
Night sounds like my dad snoring.
Night smells like a teddy bear.
Night feels like a blanket in my hand.
Night tastes like ice cream for dessert.

Nirvana Williams (6)
Bessacarr Primary School, Bessacarr

Night Poem

In the night I can see owls on hollow trees
The night sounds like rain falling
The night feels like cold ice
The night smells like candles burning
The night tastes like a warm dinner.

Maurycy Szmyt (6)
Bessacarr Primary School, Bessacarr

Night

Night looks like a big glowing moon
Night sounds like a mouse squeaking
Night smells like warm milk
Night feels like a soft blanket
Night tastes like chicken and Yorkshire pudding.

Krystal Wallis (6)
Bessacarr Primary School, Bessacarr

Night Poem

N octurnal foxes come out at night
I hear owls hooting
G limmering stars are the brightest thing
H edgehogs are prickly
T rees sway at night.

Oliver Milnthorp (6)
Bessacarr Primary School, Bessacarr

Night Poem

N ight is spooky

I t is dark, I am scared

G o to bed at night

H edgehogs come out at night

T all, terrifying monsters are in my head.

Dottie Green (6)

Bessacarr Primary School, Bessacarr

Night Poem

I see nocturnal animals at night
Like a hooting owl with his talons
I hear wolves howling
I don't hear owls hunting
I am cuddling my teddies in bed.

Henry Sritharan (6)
Bessacarr Primary School, Bessacarr

Night Poem

At night I hear wolves growling
I hear owls hooting
At night I see foxes looking in the bin
I can smell pizza cooking in the oven
I taste hot chocolate.

Michael Fox (6)
Bessacarr Primary School, Bessacarr

Night Poem

N octurnal animals come out at night
I love the night
G hosts are scary
H edgehogs come out at night
T able for snacks.

Jesse Lovell (6)
Bessacarr Primary School, Bessacarr

Night Poem

Night feels like cold water in a pool
Night smells like burning bonfires in the sky
Night looks like a dark room
Night tastes like yummy hot chocolate.

Jan Puchalski (6)
Bessacarr Primary School, Bessacarr

Night Poem

N obody comes out at night
I t is spooky
G o to bed at night
H edgehogs come out at night
T ime to go to sleep.

Maryam Hussain (6)
Bessacarr Primary School, Bessacarr

Night Poem

I see fiery stars that twinkle in the night
I hear people snoring loud
I feel my soft teddy bear
I smell lots of clean smoke in the dark blue sky.

Barnabas Harewood (6)
Bessacarr Primary School, Bessacarr

Night Poem

I see nocturnal animals come out at night
They like the dark
I hear a tu-whit tu-whoo from the owls
The stars are out at night.

Gwendoline Kwok (6)
Bessacarr Primary School, Bessacarr

Night Poem

At night I can see shiny bright stars
At night I can hear bats
At night I can smell hot chocolate
At night I can feel my bunny.

Isabelle Yeomans (6)
Bessacarr Primary School, Bessacarr

Night Poem

At night I can see stars
At night I can hear the king
I can smell and taste warm milk.

Alex Galea (6)
Bessacarr Primary School, Bessacarr

Autumn Seasons

I can see autumn leaves falling down.
I can feel the autumn breeze.
I can hear shiny conkers bumping down the trees,
they make a clinging noise while they bump down.
I can feel the wind blowing in my face, it makes a
whooping noise that I love very much.
I can smell lovely spicy gingerbread cooking in the
oven that makes a wonderful smell.
I can taste orange pumpkins that I love very much.

Mariam Tovmasyan (6)
Connaught House School, Westminster

My Five Senses In Autumn

I can see colourful trees, fresh grass and curious squirrels.
I can hear relaxing birdsong, the trees swaying and fresh rain dripping.
I can feel the cool breeze, earthy grass and warm sunshine.
I can smell nice gingerbread, hearty soup and all that fruit that has been harvested.
I can taste all the autumn air.

Calvin Dlubac (7)
Connaught House School, Westminster

Autumn Changes

A utumn changes weather
U nder crunchy leaves there is green grass
T he nights get longer and the days get shorter
U nusual sounds are made by the leaves that have been growing in spring
M any new sounds are made by animals
N ature has been changed by autumn.

Nayel Zubair (6)
Connaught House School, Westminster

Autumn Is All Around Me

I can see the crunchy leaves are changing colours on the golden brown trees.
I can hear the beautiful tweeting in the forest by the bluebirds.
I can feel the cold breeze on my jacket.
I can smell the autumn flowers on the green grass.
I can taste my wheat bar in the forest on the bench.

Aria Gamage (6)
Connaught House School, Westminster

The Farm Harvest In October

I can see a combine harvester in the wheat with its big wheels.
I can hear the engine of the combine harvester.
I can feel the soft wheat in the field on the farm.
I can smell the soft wheat in the field on the farm.
I can taste the gingerbread men in the oven.

James Williamson (6)
Connaught House School, Westminster

The Man Climbing A Tree

A man is waiting until the sun rises
U sually the sun rises late
T he man is farming corn
U nder the umbrella there is a squirrel
M an that was hard climbing that tree
N ever touch that squirrel again.

Emeer Hamita (7)
Connaught House School, Westminster

Autumn Colours

A utumn is all around me
U mbrellas needed all the time
T he leaves fall, crunchy and crumbly
U nder my feet, I can hear crunchy leaves
M ostly the leaves change colours
N ice breath I see.

Maxim Tinel (6)
Connaught House School, Westminster

Autumn Time

A utumn is when pumpkins grow
U nder the leaves there are acorns
T he rain and windy trees
U nder the colourful trees there are birds
M y hedge is spiky
N ature is amazing.

Lara Sofola (6)
Connaught House School, Westminster

Autumn Spices

I can see shiny conkers on the floor.
I can hear curious squirrels looking for food.
I can feel the strong wind blowing.
I can smell sweet gingerbread cooking.
I can taste sweet cold pumpkin.

Allegra Kandel (6)
Connaught House School, Westminster

Autumn Colours

I can see some fresh grass.
I can hear the birds singing loudly.
I can feel a cosy, warm jacket.
I can smell some spicy gingerbread.
I can taste some warm hearty soup.

Maxine Gothland (6)

Connaught House School, Westminster

Autumn Colours

I can see the fresh rain.
I can hear the relaxing birdsong.
I can feel my very cosy jacket.
I can smell the very spicy gingerbread.
I can taste the hearty soup.

Mikayla Mizrahi (7)
Connaught House School, Westminster

My Senses

I can hear the birds sing
The cat miaow
I can hear the phone ring
I can hear you.

I can see the grass grow
The bright stars
The yellow moon
I can see the white snow
I can see you.

I can smell the tasty meat
The fresh bread
The pretty flowers
I can smell your dirty feet
I can smell you.

I can touch the soft grass
The cold ice
The wet rain
I can touch the smooth glass
I can touch you.

I can taste the crispy apple
The chocolate bar
The cream cake
I can taste the fresh pineapple
I can taste you.

Prabhnam

Guru Nanak Sikh Academy, Hayes

The Poetry Bus

The bus is going to a secret place called Gurfateh's secret town
I sit near the window
The magical journey has started
I see farms, fields, roads, rivers, mountains and crowds through the window
The poetry bus arrives at its first stop
It is called Gurfateh's secret town
There are so many toys, rides, a wagon, a PS4 there.
I really enjoy the ride on the Poetry Bus.

Gurfateh Sandhu (6)
Guru Nanak Sikh Academy, Hayes

Who Am I?

Don't go far
I'll miss you
Moon is white
I'll hug you tight
Please don't go out of my sight
'Cause I am your Mr Right!
Who am I?

Answer: Your soulmate.

Angad Vig (5)
Guru Nanak Sikh Academy, Hayes

My Teddy Bear

I love my teddy bear
He has brown hair
My teddy is small and he has no fear
Teddy shares his toys and plays fair
Teddy bear and Amitoj are a cute pair!

Amitoj Dhariwal (5)
Guru Nanak Sikh Academy, Hayes

Mr Noah's Animal Riddle

I have a long neck, long legs and a soft, furry, spotty body.

I make a loud sound that nobody can hear.

Sometimes I walk but normally I gallop.

My voice can't be heard by humans.

I live in a warm climate in Africa.

I eat green plants and small leaves.

I am a mammal because I breathe air and have babies.

My voice can't be heard by humans.

What am I?

Answer: A giraffe.

Aidan Louie (6)
Mora Primary School, Cricklewood

Mr Noah's Animal Riddle

I have lots of big, round dots and I squeak quietly.
When I want to, I can gallop quickly from up high
on top of the trees.
I live in the Sahara Desert in Africa where it is
incredibly warm.
I eat small, green, nutritious and shiny leaves.
I'm a herbivore and a mammal.
I have got a tongue that will never have a hole in
it.
What am I?

Answer: A giraffe.

Theodoro Micoli Rossoni (6)
Mora Primary School, Cricklewood

Mr Noah's Animal Riddle

I look like a little bear and a wolf.
I am fluffy.
I move like a dog.
I live on the coast of Australia and Tasmania.
I eat rabbits and wallabies.
I am a mammal and I have babies.
I am the biggest carnivore marsupial.
I can crunch bones and I am mean.
I fight over who gets the best part of the meat.
What am I?

Answer: A Tasmanian devil.

Zakariya Khan (6)
Mora Primary School, Cricklewood

Mr Noah's Animal Riddle

I have black, smooth fur and small feet.
I make loud sounds like this: *oo-oo aa-aa!*
When I want to I can move fast if a predator comes to eat me.
I live in a jungle where there are a lot of spiky trees and windy air.
I am a mammal because I drink milk from my mum.
Did you know I'm related to gorillas?
What am I?

Answer: A monkey.

Eesa Hannan (7)
Mora Primary School, Cricklewood

Mr Noah's Animal Riddle

I am small and cute.
I am also hairy.
Sometimes I yap when someone is at the door.
When I move I run.
I live in a house and a garden.
I eat bones, leftovers and treats.
I am a mammal and I have babies.
I drink my mum's milk.
I am an omnivore.
I like chewing and I have canine teeth.
What am I?

Answer: A dog.

Klara Molodtsov Hay (6)
Mora Primary School, Cricklewood

Mr Noah's Animal Riddle

I am grey, big and cute.
I squeak and click.
I jump when I'm excited.
I spin when I come out.
I live in the sea and the ocean.
I eat fish, squid and crabs.
I am a mammal and I drink milk from my mum.
I am a carnivore because I eat fish, squid and crabs.
I can live for 70 years.
What am I?

Answer: A dolphin.

Emilia Savicka (7)
Mora Primary School, Cricklewood

Mr Noah's Animal Riddle

I have a long snout and I am bumpy.
I hiss, cackle and screech.
When I hunt I creep or swim towards my prey.
I live in the streams of India and Nepal.
I eat dolphin fish, tortoises and cichlids.
I am a reptile or crocodilian and I lay eggs.
Sometimes I can have ninety-five babies in one nest.
What am I?

Answer: A gharial.

Theo Ball (6)
Mora Primary School, Cricklewood

Mr Noah's Animal Riddle

I'm a family member of a donkey.
I feel so soft.
When I'm happy I neigh.
I gallop.
I live on a farm in Europe.
When I'm hungry I eat hay, grass and carrots.
I am a mammal.
I have live babies.
They are called foals.
I drink milk from my mum.
I am a herbivore.
What am I?

Answer: A horse.

Michelin Reyes (6)
Mora Primary School, Cricklewood

Mr Noah's Animal Riddle

I have a long yellow mane and yellow fur.
I growl very loudly in the night.
When I want to I can run really fast.
I live in the Savanna Desert in Africa and it is very hot.
I eat black nutritious zebras with stripes.
I am a mammal.
I have sharp teeth to crunch through my fleshy food.
What am I?

Answer: A lion.

Hala Khan (6)
Mora Primary School, Cricklewood

Mr Noah's Animal Riddle

I am very fluffy.
I have an enormous voice.
I am feathery.
I have a yellow beak.
I am an omnivore.
I eat leaves, slugs and worms.
I can fly away.
I live in two places.
I make noise and stand on one leg.
When I get hurt I go home.
I am a type of bird.
What am I?

Answer: A pigeon.

Bakr Alnzal (6)
Mora Primary School, Cricklewood

Mr Noah's Animal Riddle

I have horns.
I have two horns.
I always hit things and I crush and I crash in Africa.
I am a mammal.
I have live babies and I'm a herbivore.
I protect my babies and I eat hay and grass.
It is so yummy.
I am big and strong.
I am grey.
What am I?

Answer: A rhino.

Omar Fayez
Mora Primary School, Cricklewood

Mr Noah's Animal Riddle

I have white fur.
I have big eyes.
I make loud noises.
When I want to I can run fast.
I live in Antarctica.
I eat bluefish.
I eat small sea wolves.
I am a mammal.
I can eat sea fish and I am the biggest type of bear
in the world.
What am I?

Answer: A polar bear.

Brian Malaj (6)
Mora Primary School, Cricklewood

Mr Noah's Animal Riddle

I have yellow and brown fur.
I have smooth, scary skin.
I growl loudly.
When I see another animal I run fast.
I live in Africa and my savannah is very warm and hot.
I eat red, raw meat and it is fresh.
I can eat my food whole.
What am I?

Answer: A cheetah.

Daniel Andrisan (6)
Mora Primary School, Cricklewood

Mr Noah's Animal Riddle

I look like a bluebird.
I have gold feathers.
I feel soft.
When I'm happy I go tweet tweet.
I move by flying.
My habitat is parks and trees.
I eat berries, nuts and mealworms.
I am a bird.
I am an omnivore.
What am I?

Answer: A goldfinch.

Oumayena Aoun (6)
Mora Primary School, Cricklewood

Mr Noah's Animal Riddle

I look like a bird.
I feel soft and feathery.
I sound like a bird.
I move like a normal bird.
I live in Antarctica.
When I am hungry I glide and swoop onto my prey.
I have great hearing.
I am a bird and I lay eggs.
What am I?

Answer: A snowy owl.

Aaron Daniel Perez (7)
Mora Primary School, Cricklewood

Mr Noah's Animal Riddle

I have a spiky back and I can camouflage.
I snap with my teeth loudly.
When I want to I can crawl out of the water.
I live in the green dark lake and I eat big pieces of humans.
I am a reptile.
I am cold-blooded.
What am I?

Answer: A crocodile.

Lovelle Cummings (7)
Mora Primary School, Cricklewood

Mr Noah's Animal Riddle

I have soft yellow fur and big blue eyes.
I have furry hair.
When I want to I can run quickly.
I live in the African jungle where it is really hot.
I eat hard brown meat.
I am a mammal, I can live up to fifty years
What am I?

Answer: A lion.

Maia Tabac (6)
Mora Primary School, Cricklewood

Mr Noah's Animal Riddle

I have orange eyes and a long neck.
I make low quiet sounds.
When I want to I can gallop fast.
I live in Africa where it is extremely hot.
I eat green leaves and tall green trees.
I am a mammal and a herbivore.
What am I?

Answer: A giraffe.

Kaydan Gibbs-Young (6)
Mora Primary School, Cricklewood

Mr Noah's Animal Riddle

I have sharp teeth and hard skin.
I snap my teeth very loudly.
When I want to I can swim in the river.
I live in the murky water.
I eat big fish and small fish.
I am a reptile.
I am cold-blooded.
What am I?

Answer: A crocodile.

Israh Alkutubi (6)
Mora Primary School, Cricklewood

Mr Noah's Animal Riddle

I am big and strong.
I am black and brown.
I grunt and I roar.
I can swing high.
I live in the jungle.
I eat grass and bananas.
I am a mammal and mammals have babies.
I am a herbivore.
What am I?

Answer: A gorilla.

Yunes Badri (7)
Mora Primary School, Cricklewood

Mr Noah's Animal Riddle

I have peach-coloured skin and legs.
I have warm skin.
When I want to I can jump.
I live in Australia.
I eat leaves that are really yummy.
I am a mammal.
I live up to twenty-three years.
What am I?

Answer: A kangaroo.

Jaicob Huxley (5)
Mora Primary School, Cricklewood

Mr Noah's Animal Riddle

I have a mane, brown eyes and smooth fur.
I make a loud roar and I can run.
I live in the savannah.
I eat red meat and nice smooth humans.
I am a mammal.
I can live up to fifty years.
What am I?

Answer: A lion.

Mohamed Mohamed (6)
Mora Primary School, Cricklewood

Mr Noah's Animal Riddle

I have white fur and I match the snow.
I have black eyes and I have a black nose.
I walk and run.
I live in the Arctic.
I love meat.
I am a carnivore.
I have a baby.
What am I?

Answer: An Arctic fox.

Salma Al Thafiri Al Ghazi (6)
Mora Primary School, Cricklewood

Mr Noah's Animal Riddle

I'm grey and I look like a friendly shark.
I click and move fast.
I live in the ocean and the sea.
I eat fish, squid and crabs.
I'm a mammal and I have babies.
What am I?

Answer: A dolphin.

Beatriz Furlan Thomaz (6)

Mora Primary School, Cricklewood

Mr Noah's Animal Riddle

I am yellow, black and soft.
I can roar and I can be very loud.
I am from Africa.
I am a carnivore.
I am a mammoth and I drink milk from my mum.
I run fast.
What am I?

Answer: A cheetah.

Abdullah Sardari (7)
Mora Primary School, Cricklewood

Mr Noah's Animal Riddle

I am grey and I am soft and cuddly.
I squeak and I hop.
I live in the forest.
I eat yummy carrots.
I am a mammal and I have live babies.
I am a herbivore.
What am I?

Answer: A rabbit.

India Goodman (7)
Mora Primary School, Cricklewood

Mr Noah's Animal Riddle

I have grey skin.
I am smooth and big.
I make loud noises.
I can run fast.
I live in the jungle.
I eat grass.
I am a mammal.
What am I?

Answer: An elephant.

Anastazija Maric (6)
Mora Primary School, Cricklewood

Mr Noah's Animal Riddle

I look like a duck.
I am feathery.
I am extinct.
I eat crabs and seeds.
I am silent.
I am an omnivore.
I can't fly.
What am I?

Answer: A dodo.

Jason Brook (6)
Mora Primary School, Cricklewood

Mr Noah's Animal Riddle

I am grey and I have small ears.
I can run and walk.
I live in a house.
I eat meat.
I am a carnivore.
What am I?

Answer: A dog.

Carmina Dragan (6)
Mora Primary School, Cricklewood

Mr Noah's Animal Riddle

I am big and grey.
I like grass.
I stomp.
I run.
What am I?

Answer: An elephant.

Zoha Jaffar (6)
Mora Primary School, Cricklewood

Mr Noah's Animal Riddle

I am black.
I run.
I live in a house.
I like cat food.
What am I?

Answer: A cat.

Isabella Pampolini De Oliveira (6)
Mora Primary School, Cricklewood

A Snowman

S nowmen are built in winter because of the snow
N o one touches a snowman
O ne of the snowmen has many friends
W hy are you so very cold?
M elting slowly it goes away
A snowman has a big carrot nose and it melts
N ever seen again and will not be built again.

Evie Rose (6)
New Horizons Children's Academy, Chatham

A Snowman

S nowmen are so very cool
N o one touches snowmen because they are cold
O ne snowman has lots of friends
W hy are you so very cold?
M elting slowly and he's gone
A cool snowman is not hot
N ever see again, he's gone.

Swayley Smith (6)
New Horizons Children's Academy, Chatham

Stick Insect

S ticky feet
T iny stick insect
I love stick insects
C limb all over
K icks legs

I see them
k **N** obbly
S ticky claws
E asy to find
C ool
T rees get climbed up.

Harrison James (6)
New Horizons Children's Academy, Chatham

Christmas

C runchy biscuits
H appy day
R eady to write your Christmas list
I love Christmas
S ing along to tunes
T ime to open presents
M usic
A lovely amazing time
S leep.

Brooke Sanders (6)
New Horizons Children's Academy, Chatham

Frankie

F ood is yummy

R unning is fun

A chocolate bar is yummy

N est with birds in

K icking and jumping

I hug my mummy

E ating food is good.

Frankie Joe Walton (6)

New Horizons Children's Academy, Chatham

Winter

Winter is the smell of the wind blowing
While it snows
Winter is the sight of the snowflakes falling from
the sky
Winter is all about having fun and spending time
with your friends and family.

Uzma Sebagala (6)

New Horizons Children's Academy, Chatham

Snow

S now is fun and happy

N ow Mum is cold in the wet and white snow

O n the red sled, I fell furthest down the white snow

W hen I went on my black sled, it was fast!

Lilah Fiddler (6)

New Horizons Children's Academy, Chatham

Snowman

S teve the snowman
N ose made from a carrot
O range and wintery
W earing a woolly scarf
M elting
A ll alone
N ow he's gone.

Sam Kitchen (6)
New Horizons Children's Academy, Chatham

Fishbowl

F ish
I love my fish
S ad fish
H appy fish
B ubbling up and down
O ver and under
W ow, slow down
L ow and high.

Archie Funnell (6)
New Horizons Children's Academy, Chatham

Friends

F riends
R eally good
I nteresting ideas
E veryone hugs
N o one gets hurt
D oing fun stuff
S illy faces they pull.

Jack Hobby (5)
New Horizons Children's Academy, Chatham

Friends

F riends
R eally good
I nteresting ideas
E veryone likes a hug
N o one gets hurt
D oing fun stuff
S miling a lot.

Erica Sanders (5) & Ava
New Horizons Children's Academy, Chatham

Friends

F riendly
R eally cool
I nteresting ideas
E veryone likes help
N o one gets hurt
D o funny stuff
S miling also.

Sofia Romanenco (5)

New Horizons Children's Academy, Chatham

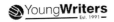
Pop

I smell a sweet pop
I share a pop, pop, pop
I taste a pop, pop, pop
I see something white
It feels soft
What is it?

Answer: Popcorn!

Grace Hider (6)
New Horizons Children's Academy, Chatham

Mummy

My mummy does the washing
My mummy does the dishes
My mummy gives me hugs
My mummy buys the curtains for the house
My mummy buys stuff for the house.

Keilan Chiverton (7)
New Horizons Children's Academy, Chatham

Panda

P retty panda
A piece of bamboo
N o other food to eat but bamboo
D oes everything
A nd loves everything.

Ruby Groves (7)
New Horizons Children's Academy, Chatham

About My Puppy

P layful every day
U nhappy sometimes
P layful
P lays like every dog can
Y awns a lot as always tired.

Esmé Dale (6)

New Horizons Children's Academy, Chatham

Puppy

P uppy likes to play
U se the bone to chew
P uppy likes to run
P uppy loves his toys
Y ou have a tail.

Marley Beale (6)
New Horizons Children's Academy, Chatham

Winter

W indy and cold
I nside the snow it's
N ot hot
T oo cold
E scaping
R eady to go.

Ayden Sabondo (6)

New Horizons Children's Academy, Chatham

Sweets

S tick
W hite sweets
E at it
E ach sweet is see-through
T idy up the wrapper
S weet.

Isabella Kerr (6)
New Horizons Children's Academy, Chatham

Pop!

I hear the pop, pop, pop
I smell all the smells
I taste the salt
It is very white
What could it be?
It's Popcorn!

Tanya Suetlomirova (6)

New Horizons Children's Academy, Chatham

Harry

H appy boy
A good boy
R eally likes bunnies
R eally likes countries
Y ummy pasta for him.

Harry McClelland (6)
New Horizons Children's Academy, Chatham

Avatar

A irbender

V illage

A vatar

T he Last Airbender

A irbender tattoo

R iver.

Leon Roadnight (6)

New Horizons Children's Academy, Chatham

Cupcakes

They are sweet
They look colourful and yummy
They smell like chocolate
They feel squishy
They are squelchy.

Ava Leishamn (6)
New Horizons Children's Academy, Chatham

What Am I?

I smell some mud
I hear a roar
I taste some fur
I see some flies
What am I?

Answer: A lion.

Fredrik Hogan (6)

New Horizons Children's Academy, Chatham

Sweets

Sweets taste sweet
Sweets are squishy
Sweets are tasty
They are delicious
They are tasty and sticky.

Imogen Still (6)
New Horizons Children's Academy, Chatham

Sylvia

S unny
Y ellow
L ovely
V iolet
I love my mum
A mazing.

Sylvia Arnold (5)
New Horizons Children's Academy, Chatham

Lion

L ions are so fast

I ncredibly fast

O n every rock a lion lays

N oisy lions.

Albie Leslie (6)

New Horizons Children's Academy, Chatham

Unicorn

Unicorn is sleepy
It is shiny
Its horn is beautiful
It lives on a rainbow
Really is a good one.

Jade Foreman (6)
New Horizons Children's Academy, Chatham

Daisy

D oing fun stuff
A mazing
I like my cousin
S miling a lot
Y ay!

Daisy Page (5)

New Horizons Children's Academy, Chatham

Lehna's Poem

I like green grass
And blueberries
I do not like apples
I love Mum and oranges and strawberries.

Lehna Buparai (6)
New Horizons Children's Academy, Chatham

Cupcakes

They taste sweet.
They look colourful.
They smell nice.
They feel soft.
They feel squishy.

Aarna Patel (6)
New Horizons Children's Academy, Chatham

Lollipops

Lollipops are sweet
And tasty
And yummy
And they are sandy
And they taste sweet.

Nicole Eze (6)
New Horizons Children's Academy, Chatham

T-Rex

T ommy T-rex
R eally loud
E veryone scared
e **X** tremely scary!

Chase Whitmore (6)
New Horizons Children's Academy, Chatham

Lion

L ions are big
I n a cage for a home
O n the hunt
N ot nice.

Charlie-Junior Blair (6)
New Horizons Children's Academy, Chatham

What Makes Me Smile?

S mile

M um

I like the shop

L ollipops

E ggs.

Ronnie Butler (5)

New Horizons Children's Academy, Chatham

My Dogs

I see funky fur
I feel a soft nose
I hear owls and I hear barks
I smell dog food.

Georgina Philpott (6)
New Horizons Children's Academy, Chatham

Bear

B ig, sharp claws
E ats honey
A ll fluffy
R eally strong.

Efren Simpson (7)
New Horizons Children's Academy, Chatham

What Makes Me Smile?

S ea
M ummy
I ce cream
L ollipop
E aster.

Eloisa Tingley-Smith (5)
New Horizons Children's Academy, Chatham

Beech

B eautiful

E ggs

E xit

C hildren

H ouse.

Busola Ogundiwin (5)

New Horizons Children's Academy, Chatham

What Makes Me Smile?

S un
M ud
I ce cream
L emon
E aster egg.

Jemima Caprice (6)

New Horizons Children's Academy, Chatham

Jack

J ack likes jelly
A mazing
C ool
K ind and smiling.

Jack Stevenson (5)
New Horizons Children's Academy, Chatham

What Makes Me Smile?

S ophie
M um
I ce cream
L ollies
E lsa.

Dorothy Brown (5)

New Horizons Children's Academy, Chatham

Cat

I can see fluffy fur
I can feel fur
I can touch the fur
I can taste fish.

Amelia Norton (6)
New Horizons Children's Academy, Chatham

What Makes Me Smile?

S ea
M ummy
I ce cream
L ions
E lsa.

Vivian Kisyova (5)
New Horizons Children's Academy, Chatham

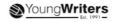

What Makes Me Smile?

S un
M um
I ce cream
L ollies
E ggs.

Sophie Goodchild (5)
New Horizons Children's Academy, Chatham

What Makes Me Smile?

S un
M um
I gloos
L ollipops
E ggs.

Aretha Yeboah-Boafo (5)
New Horizons Children's Academy, Chatham

What Makes Me Smile?

S un
M um
I ce cream
L emons
E lsa.

Cassia (5)

New Horizons Children's Academy, Chatham

Aston

A rtist

S porty

T ag

O lder

N inja.

Aston Edwards (5)

New Horizons Children's Academy, Chatham

What Is It?

I see something big
It is scaly
What could it be?
It's a dinosaur.

Muaaz Mazeen (6)

New Horizons Children's Academy, Chatham

What Makes Me Smile?

S un

M um

I ce cream

L ions

E ggs.

Sofia Georgieva (5)

New Horizons Children's Academy, Chatham

What Makes Me Smile?

S unshine

M um

I ce

L ove

E ggs.

Sofia B (5)

New Horizons Children's Academy, Chatham

What Makes Me Smile?

S un
M um
I ce
L ollipop
E ggs.

Jessica (5)
New Horizons Children's Academy, Chatham

What Makes Me Smile?

S un
M um
I ce
L olly
E ggs.

Maksimilian Kosenkov (5)
New Horizons Children's Academy, Chatham